Usborne

Lots of things to spot in the Town

Written by Hazel Maskell

Illustrated by Sigrid Martinez

Designed by Catherine-Anne MacKinnon and Helen Lee

Edited by Ruth Brocklehurst

Each big scene in this book shows a different part of a busy town. There are lots of things to spot and talk about on each page, and games to play.

These six animals live in the town.
They appear in every scene. Can you find them all?

Lenny the lion
loves skateboarding.

Hetty the hippo
is very fond of food.

Percy the penguin
is a photographer.

Kai the koala
reads a lot.

Bernie the badger
is an artist.

Zara the zebra
likes to go shopping.

There's a red
balloon to spot in
every scene too.

Contents

In the Town Square

Spot 3 differences between these statues.

LIBRARY

Find my 5 lost library books.

How many of each of these things can you count?

 town flags

 milkshakes

 trees tomatoes 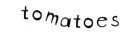 lamp posts backpacks

5

Going Shopping

Where can I get my hair cut?

Where can I catch a taxi?

Hairdressers

Dress to Impress

Shoes

Sports

Open

Can you find each of these things?

6

 menu

 rocket

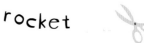 scissors

 red shirt

shopping bags

 purple boots

The Sports Ground

How many of each of these things can you find?

yellow flags | Poles | cones

 orange T-shirts   purple bottles   headbands

At the Market

How many passengers can you see on the bus?

The Lunch Stall

Chic Clothes

Pancakes

Cheese

Where can I buy a T-shirt?

Can you help Hetty find these things in the market?

 oranges

 bread

 fish   eggs   honey   cheese

11

Winter Time

Where can I buy a balloon?

Which 3 skaters are wearing matching clothes?

Hot Chocolate

How many of each of these things can you find?

 red flags

 lanterns

 wreaths sleds spotted scarves hot drinks

At the Station

Bus Station

Town Square

Can you spot **4** builders wearing yellow hats?

News Hu

= Business train =

How many of my passengers can you count wearing hats?

Can you find each of these things?

 red suitcase

 binoculars

 sandwich

 green car

 train times

 ticket

Time for School

How many of each of these things can you find?

 scooters

 school bag

Going Swimming

Who's wearing the same swimsuit as me?

Where are the showers?

How many of each of these things can you find? pool noodles red swim caps

 diving masks sun loungers · rubber ducks ● balls

In the Park

How many bees can you count?

How many fish can you spot in the pond?

Boat hut

Can you find each of these things?

 wheelbarrow lawn mower

 picnic basket toy boat gazebo watering can

21

Town Parade

How many clowns with red noses can you see?

Find the dancer who is wearing a yellow headband.

Can you find each of these things?

circus tent

sports cup

22

Games

Look back through the scenes in the book to spot these things.

Where can you find these birds?

9 white pigeons across seven scenes

Duck and 6 ducklings in one scene

5 seagulls in one scene

Can you spot these toys?

Jack-in-a-box

Elephants

Fish

Find these things for sale!

T-shirt with toadstool picture

Bat

Blue shoes

Wedding cake

Can you find these musical instruments?

French horn

Piano

Double bass

Where can you see these characters?

Dentist

Firefighters

Swim instructor

Postman

Roadworkers

Teacher

24

Use the stickers to dress us.

Kai
the koala

Bernie
the badger

Zara
the zebra

Draw lines to match each of these with its opposite.

OPPOSITES

Old   Light   Summer   Happy   Hot

Winter   Sad   Young   Dark   Cold

SMALL AND BIG

Use the stickers to put these things in order of size, from smallest to biggest.

Then, fill us in with crayons or pencils.

Lenny the lion

Hetty the hippo

Percy the penguin

SPOT THE DIFFERENCE

Find 5 differences between these pictures.

Add to this street scene using the stickers.

Answers

4-5 In the Town Square

There are 3 town flags, 4 milkshakes, 2 trees, 8 tomatoes, 3 lamp posts and 5 backpacks.

Differences:

 Library books

 Mayor

6-7 Going shopping

You can get a haircut in the hairdressers.
Zara can buy a new hat in 'Dress to Impress'.

Castle

 Menu

 Rocket

Scissors

 Red shirt

 Shopping bags

 Purple boots

 Postcards

 Taxi stand

8-9 The Sports Ground

There are 2 yellow flags, 4 poles, 8 cones, 5 orange T-shirts, 3 purple bottles and 6 headbands. There are 5 players in each team.

This runner is winning the race.

 Orange balls

 Bananas for sale

 Whistle

10-11 At the Market

There are 4 pumpkins. There are 2 passengers on the bus.

 Oranges

 Bread

 Fish

 Eggs

 Honey

Cheese

 T-shirt seller

Matching plants

12-13 Winter Time

There are 3 red flags, 7 lanterns, 8 wreaths, 4 sleds, 6 spotted scarves and 6 hot drinks. There are 10 lights on the tree.

 Matching hats

 Balloon seller

Skaters wearing matching clothes

Differences:

14-15 At the Station

Lenny is driving the crane. 5 passengers are wearing hats.
It is 1 o'clock.

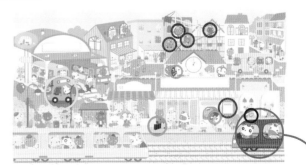

This train is going to the beach.

 Red suitcase

 Binoculars

Sandwich

Green car

Train times

 Ticket

 Builders in yellow hats

16-17 Time for School

There are 4 scooters, 6 school bags, 3 guitar cases, 4 apples, 3 balls and 5 butterflies.

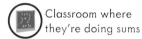 Classroom where they're doing sums

 School bell

 Yellow hoops

18-19 Going Swimming

There are 4 pool noodles, 5 red swim caps, 3 diving masks, 8 sun loungers, 3 rubber ducks and 5 balls.
There are 4 babies in the little pool.

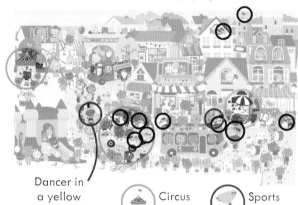

 Matching swimsuits

 Showers

Highest diving board

20-21 In the Park

There are 6 bees. There are 5 fish in the pond. Hetty is playing the trumpet.

You can buy an ice cream here.

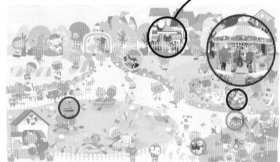

 Wheelbarrow

 Lawn mower

 Picnic basket

 Toy boat

 Gazebo

 Watering can

22-23 Town parade

There are 4 clowns. Zara and Kai are playing the drums.

Dancer in a yellow headband

 Circus tent

 Sports cup

 Ice cream cart

 Mayor's car

Matching flags

Games

BIRDS

White pigeons: 1 each on pages 5, 7, 16, 21 and 22; 2 each on pages 11 and 14. Duck and ducklings: page 21. Seagulls: pages 18-19.

MUSICAL INSTRUMENTS

French horn: page 23. Piano: page 16.
Double bass: page 21.

TOYS

Jack-in-a-box: page 7. Elephants: page 11.
Fish: page 19.

SHOPS

Toadstool T-shirt: page 10. Bat: page 6.
Blue shoes: page 6. Wedding cake: page 11.

CHARACTERS

Dentist: page 6. Firefighters: page 22.
Swim instructor: page 18. Postman: page 17.
Roadworkers: page 7. Teacher: page 17.

MAZE

—— To the circus
—— To the sports ground
—— To the ice cream seller

OPPOSITES

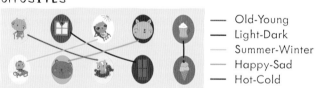

—— Old-Young
—— Light-Dark
—— Summer-Winter
—— Happy-Sad
—— Hot-Cold

SMALL AND BIG

Bee   Ball   Bicycle   Tree   Castle

SPOT THE DIFFERENCES

Differences: ⭕

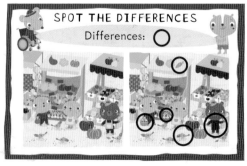